WORKBOOK D
BASIC READING

GLENN McCRACKEN
New Castle, Pennsylvania

CHARLES C. WALCUTT
Queens College, Flushing, New York

in collaboration with

MARY F. BOND

STATE COLLEGE AT FRAMINGHAM, FRAMINGHAM, MASSACHUSETTS

ESTHER FAIRCLOTH

MALDEN PUBLIC SCHOOLS, MALDEN, MASSACHUSETTS

J. B. LIPPINCOTT COMPANY
PHILADELPHIA, NEW YORK

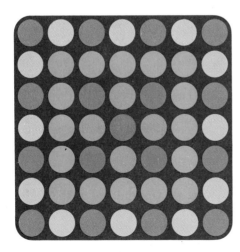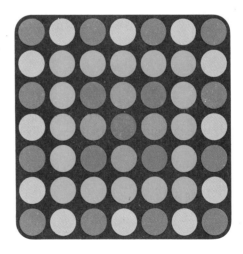

CONTENTS

ISBN—0-397-43549-5

Draw a line around the words with short vowels.

stand	since	fence	ran	six
make	pond	dance	mend	ten
went	safe	name	fair	time
dime	help	and	like	not
Tom	did	than	licking	just
Tim	join	came	with	greedy
him	his	hill	boy	next
told	man	nice	rushed	really
then	wise	big	grass	that
bit	day	running	but	fun
after	long	tried	big	moist
sheep	from	flock	grazing	just

Use: After page 1 in the text.
Purpose: To develop independent recognition of short vowel words in a group situation.
NOTE: The teacher should read the directions on each page with the children before having them work independently.

Draw a line around the related words.

1.	2.	3.	4.	5.
green	foot	worker	hoist	annoyed
yellow	join	shepherd	him	bothered
when	hand	farmer	lift	happy
red	arm	home	raise	displeased

6.	7.	8.	9.	10.
cat	soft	feed	trees	tended
wolf	rushed	eat	enjoy	spend
child	hurried	soil	forest	cared for
lion	ran	graze	woods	minded

11.	12.	13.	14.	15.
commotion	foot	wolf	his	grade
truth	trick	same	village	thin
trouble	joke	alike	town	class
noise	game	twins	city	group

16.	17.	18.	19.	20.
protect	take	much	mouth	say
care	steal	meal	lips	tell
start	rob	lunch	hair	take
defend	give	snack	teeth	mention

Use: After page 1 in the text.
Purpose: To develop the ability to select words in a group of words which have similar meaning.

Which word comes first in the alphabet?   Put it in column 1.
Then put the other two words in order in columns 2 and 3.

	1	2	3
	_____	_____	_____
	_____	_____	_____
1. cost lost frost	_____	_____	_____
	_____	_____	_____
2. not hot got	_____	_____	_____
	_____	_____	_____
3. long song dong	_____	_____	_____
	_____	_____	_____
4. bold cold hold	_____	_____	_____
	_____	_____	_____
5. no go so	_____	_____	_____
	_____	_____	_____
6. rode code goat	_____	_____	_____

Use: After page 1 in the text.
Purpose: To provide an experience with alphabetical order, using words containing long and short **o** phonemes/graphemes.

Draw a line around the words that do not have a long **o** sound.
Underline all the words that do have the long **o** sound.

1.	2.	3.	4.	5.
hope	not	won't	no	cot
hop	note	don't	go	boat
cold	rope	doll	on	coat

6.	7.	8.	9.	10.
rock	joke	hot	rose	frog
bold	got	broke	hose	four
fold	choke	float	fog	sore

11.	12.	13.	14.	15.
floor	Joe	load	top	bolder
shop	toe	spot	old	golden
door	shot	gold	hold	log

16.	17.	18.	19.	20.
toad	rode	drop	going	stole
road	crop	stolen	gone	top
lost	code	swollen	wore	pole

Use: After page 1 in the text.
Purpose: This activity reviews long **o** phonemes.

4

Match the two parts of the sentences by drawing connecting lines.

Did you join   made loud noises.

The happy children   jingled in my pocket.

The silver coins   the Boy Scouts?

The oil will   broiled over the coals.

Can you hear   spoil your dress.

The chops were   the girl's sweet voice?

Match the word or group of words that have almost the same meaning.

1. oyster	happy	1. coin	damp
2. elbow joint	cook	2. boil	loud
3. joyful	shellfish	3. moist	penny
4. broil	part of the arm	4. enjoy	selection
5. soiled	child	5. noisy	cook in water
6. boy	dirty	6. choice	like

Use: After page 6 in the text.
Purpose: To provide a review of words having **oi** and **oy** phonemes in context as well as in test of meaning.

Cross out the word that does not belong.   Put that word on the lines.

_____

1. boy   child   fox   baby   _____

2. Joyce   Tom   Sally   Mary   _____

3. joy   gloom   gladness   happiness   _____

4. muff   loud   noisy   banging   _____

5. damp   moist   wet   ink   _____

6. apple   royal   palace   throne   _____

7. join   trick   connect   meet   _____

Use: After page 6 in the text.
Purpose: This activity develops the ability to select a word which is dissimilar in meaning to a group of words.

6

Find the word that is the opposite of the word at the left.
What number is it?   Put that number on the line.
Look at the first one.

give	_3_	1. tiny
opened	_____	2. poorest
inside	_____	3. take
found	_____	4. lost
richest	_____	5. closed
huge	_____	6. outside

greedy	_____	1. big
little	_____	2. unused
always	_____	3. sharing
sooner	_____	4. later
used	_____	5. front
back	_____	6. never

wife	_____	1. herself
his	_____	2. husband
himself	_____	3. sadly
cured	_____	4. hers
happily	_____	5. empty
filled	_____	6. sick

Use: After page 6 in the text.
Purpose: To develop word meaning through antonyms.

Fill in the fourth word.

1. cake   — eat   milk   — <u>   drink   </u>

2. girl   — mother   boy   — <u> father </u>

3. Ruth   — girl   Luke   — _____

4. winter — cold   summer — _____

5. kitten — cat   puppy   — _____

6. six   — five   ten   — _____

7. finger — hand   toe   — _____

Use: After pages 6 and 7 in the text.
Purpose: To develop the ability to arrange related ideas independently.

Complete each sentence.   Put the correct word on the lines.

_____

_____

1. Will you come and _____ the group?   **joy**   **join**

_____

_____

2. Don't _____ your finger at everything.   **point**   **paint**

_____

_____

3. Her _____ is very sweet.   **voice**   **post**

_____

_____

4. A penny is called a _____.   **cold**   **coin**

_____

_____

5. Keep the food cold, or it will _____.   **spool**   **spoil**

Draw a line around each boy's name.		Draw a line around each girl's name.	
Tom	Roy	Cathy	Joyce
Ann	Fred	Ned	Betty
Dan	Pammy	Ellen	Mike
And	Kate	Teddy	Patty

Use: After page 7 in the text.
Purpose: To give further practice in recognition of words containing the **oi** and **oy** phonemes/graphemes.

9

Vocabulary Test

since	circus	large	stage	slice
cider	circle	huge	page	face
celery	cane	cage	rage	nice
attention	direction	tool	spool	good
admission	collection	poor	cool	took
vacation	confusion	pool	food	shook
bowed	growing	flow	store	four
bowl	snowing	growl	flower	fourteen
bowing	slower	shower	float	fourth
sheep	clear	fine	shout	boy
squeeze	fear	finer	shower	toys
sneeze	tears	finest	stout	store
boys	soil	enjoy	joint	joy
noise	oil	annoy	coin	toy
nose	boil	oyster	voice	Roy

Use: After page 7 in the text. (See back cover of Teacher's Edition.)
Purpose: Vocabulary Test.

10

Read each sentence and draw a line around the correct word.
Put the word on the blank lines.

_____

_____   few

                                      pew

1. A bench in a church is called a _____.

_____

                                      you

_____   dew

2. The dampness on the grass is called _____.

_____

                                      stew

_____   true

3. Mother boiled meat and made a _____.

_____

                                      guess

_____   grew

4. Bob _____ so tall that his clothes didn't fit.

_____

                                      grew

_____   crew

5. The _____ will sail the boat.

_____

                                      chew

_____   gym

6. We do not _____ gum in school.

_____

                                      flour

_____   flew

7. We _____ like birds in the giant plane.

Use: After page 8 in the text.
Purpose: To strengthen ability to read, write, spell, and fix meanings of **ew** words.

Draw a line under the two sentences where the underlined words
mean the same or nearly the same.

He <u>drew</u> a picture of a horse.

The farmer <u>drew</u> the cool water from the well.

She <u>drew</u> a house with trees and birds.

The <u>crew</u> of men were on the ship.

The barber gave him a <u>crew</u> cut.

The leader liked his <u>crew</u> of men.

It was nice and cool down by the <u>pool</u>.

He got a <u>pool</u> table for his birthday.

He went wading in the <u>pool</u>.

The lines he drew were nice and <u>even</u>.

You may <u>even</u> say he was the smartest.

With a ruler he made five <u>even</u> lines.

The king <u>ruled</u> the land with love.

He <u>ruled</u> the paper carefully.

The queen <u>ruled</u> as soon as she was crowned.

Use: After page 8 in the text.
Purpose: This activity promotes ability to detect word meanings. The same word has different meanings.

Put the numbers **1, 2,** or **3** on the blank lines so that
the sentences are in the correct order (**1—2—3.**)

Then she had only seven cents to spend. ____

Mary had ten cents for candy. ____

Mary spent three cents. ____

When they got home they were tired. ____

They had a good time at the circus. ____

The children rode on the bus to the circus. ____

For five days they worked hard in school. ____

Tom and Ruth went to church on the first day of the week. ____

On the last day they played with other children. ____

Mother rushed out to bring in the clothes. ____

Then it began to rain very hard. ____

Mother put the clothes out to dry. ____

Last year Sue was in kindergarten. ____

Next year she will be in the second grade. ____

This year she is in the first grade. ____

Use: After page 8 in the text.
Purpose: This activity promotes the ability to arrange three related ideas in sequence.

Put these in proper sequence by numbering the boxes.

"It is a pity my legs grew so slim." □

"Few animals have such horns as mine," he said. □

It was a nice clear morning. □

At that moment a hunter blew his horn. □

A beautiful deer was drinking from a pool. □

Finally, he worked his way free, just in time. □

Away bounded the deer. □

The hunter aimed his arrow at the deer. □

"My legs helped me escape," he said. □

His beautiful antlers got snarled in some branches. □

Use: After page 12 in the text.
Purpose: Checking sequence understanding of the story "The Deer and the Hunter."

14

Draw a line around the two words of opposite meanings.
Read across the page.

Example: (hot) — (cold)

big	see	mine	his
sit	stay	store	stand
sad	hide	fence	seek
sit	smile	frown	five
wife	hat	husband	happy
wide	narrow	big	boy
front	fox	behind	four

box	boy	girl	give
mats	man	lady	lamp
died	dust	bad	born
well	sick	soft	sat
wet	well	did	dry
he	here	there	this
since	star	stop	start
hand	foot	fox	has

Use: After page 12 in the text.
Purpose: To give further practice in recognizing antonyms.

Draw a line around the rhyming words.

1. sparrow narrow yelling	**2.** grow drew grew	**3.** few pin pew	**4.** chew this threw	**5.** legs begs sings	**6.** stew dew does
7. feast beauty beast	**8.** beautiful flew new	**9.** soon true blew	**10.** threw glue there	**11.** June took tune	**12.** flew mule due
13. Sue fruit suit	**14.** rule ruler fool	**15.** truth boots booth	**16.** buy boy joy	**17.** pond point joint	**18.** took broil toil
19. soon soil spoil	**20.** four spot pour	**21.** your young sung	**22.** down trouble double	**23.** sour sound round	**24.** count cost mount

Use: After pages 9-12 in the text.
Purpose: To test auditory and visual recognition of **ew** and **eau** words, and review.

Put the sentences in correct order by numbering the boxes.
Then draw a picture in each box below to tell about the story.

The boys said he was too little.　☐

But no one wanted to play with him.　☐

Martin was a little boy who liked to play baseball.　☐

So Martin's brother played with him.　☐

One big dog liked this little dog, Tom.　☐

The two went everywhere.　☐

Once there was a tiny dog named Tom.　☐

One day the big dog moved away and this made
Tom feel very lonely.　☐

Use: After page 13 in the text.
Purpose: To provide further opportunity to see sequential order in various stories.

Draw a line around the words that are classified under the titles.

Time		Size		Looks	
moment	antlers	tall	said	beautiful	grand
day	summer	slim	large	handsome	carry

Place		Parts of the Body		Animals	
legs	here	arms	legs	deer	sheep
home	there	too	toes	antlers	pigs

Playthings		Sadness		Joy	
best	ball	hurt	pain	gladness	fun
doll	blocks	will	pity	feet	happiness

Draw a line around the word of nearly opposite meaning of the first word.

few	many	man	grew	flew	crew	to
beautiful	small	ugly	bet	bed	better	best
ground	grass	grab	grand	ship	shut	sky
narrow	win	wind	sparrow	wide	with	winter
more	less	lend	let's	leg	move	love
near	fan	farm	farmer	far	nest	net
useful	use	us	uncle	up	is	useless
most	more	mat	mop	let	least	letter

Use: After page 13 in the text.
Purpose: Classifying objects by recognizing word meanings.

Underline the words of opposite meanings.
Put the two words on the blank lines.

1. I like to draw pictures.
   I hate to go out in the snow.

   _____   _____

   _____   _____

   _____   _____

2. This meat is raw.
   I ate the cooked food.

   _____   _____

   _____   _____

   _____   _____

3. He woke up at dawn.
   That evening he was very tired.

   _____   _____

   _____   _____

   _____   _____

4. My daughter has long yellow hair.
   My son has yellow hair, too.

   _____   _____

   _____   _____

   _____   _____

5. He caught three fish yesterday.
   He freed the little ones.

   _____   _____

   _____   _____

   _____   _____

Use: After page 14 in the text.
Purpose: To develop recognition of words of nearly opposite meanings.

19

Draw a line under the two sentences where the underlined words
have the same meaning.

They <u>saw</u> the stores where toys were sold.

This <u>saw</u> is so dull it will not cut wood.

The man <u>saw</u> the awful accident.

The eagle's <u>claws</u> were very long.

The dog's <u>claws</u> need to be cut.

The little kitten <u>claws</u> the furniture.

She had a vacation last <u>spring</u>.

In the <u>spring</u> we see pussy willows.

They took fresh water from the <u>spring</u>.

I want to give her a <u>fair</u> mark.

This is such a beautiful, <u>fair</u> day.

Tomorrow will be <u>fair</u> and warmer.

I will <u>train</u> the children every day.

He will have to <u>train</u> the dog.

I must hurry to catch the last <u>train</u>.

The <u>pool</u> table is large and green.

The <u>pool</u> is good to sail boats in.

They went wading in the <u>pool</u>.

Use: After page 14 in the text.
Purpose: Classification of ideas according to similar meaningful sentences.

20

Put the word on the lines to make a good sentence.
Cross out the word below as you put it on the lines.

_____

1. They _____ the children playing tag.

2. That is a _____ and you must follow it.

3. The eagle's _____ are long and sharp.

law   **claws**   **saw**

_____

4. The _____ of the book is visiting here.

5. This house needs _____ at the windows.

6. This cup and _____ are very pretty.

saucer   **author**   **awnings**

Use: After page 14 in the text.
Purpose: To provide further practice in discriminating use of **aw** and **au** words.

21

Study the first two words of each group. Read the two sentences
and write the correct words on the blank lines.

1. **paws**   **pause**

_____

_____

The kitten's _____ are soft and silky.

_____

_____

Do not _____ so much when you read.

2. **all**   **awl**

_____

_____

I will invite _____ the children to the party.

_____

_____

An _____ is a tool for punching small holes.

3. **Don**   **dawn**

_____

_____

My little brother _____ goes to the park.

_____

_____

He got up at the crack of _____.

Use: After page 14 in the text.
Purpose: To provide practice in recognition of homonyms and similar sounding words using many **aw** and **au** words.

Read the story silently.   Follow the directions at the end.

One day Mrs. Smith and her daughter, Ellen, went visiting a family. There were six children.   Ellen felt that she was going to have a very good day.

The twins, Paul and Paula, were Ellen's age, seven years old. Bob and Ann were older.   Then there was the little daughter, Ruth, who was six, and the baby, who was just crawling around on the floor.

Ellen ran and jumped and rolled a hoop with the children. Paul took some fishing rods, and they went down to the brook to fish. Bob and Paul taught Ellen how to fish.   It was fun, but Ellen didn't catch any fish. Her clothes were wet, but it wasn't Ellen's fault because children all get splashed when they fish.

The five children went back to the house, but they paused to rest several times.

It was soon time to go home so Mrs. Smith put a shawl around Ellen who yawned all the way home.   She had had such a wonderful time with so many children!

Underline all the words with **au** or **aw** that you can find in the story.
Pick one of each to write below.

au	**aw**
_____	_____
_____	_____
_____	_____

Use: After page 17 in the text.
Purpose: To provide for use of **aw** and **au** words in context.

Read each sentence.   Read each question.   Underline the words that answer each question.

1. The grass was tall,
   so Bob mowed the lawn.

   What did Bob do?

2. Mr. Brown put up the awning
   to keep out the sun.

   What did Mr. Brown do?

3. The animal crawled into the
   hole to keep warm.

   Where did the animal crawl?

4. Birds go south because
   days grow cold.

   Why do birds go south?

5. When the hawk came near,
   the birds flew away.

   What flew away?

6. The children went swimming
   in the pond.

   Where did the children go?

7. In the play, Dawn was dressed
   like a pirate.

   How was Dawn dressed?

8. My daughter, Jane, is in
   the sixth grade.

   Who is in the sixth grade?

Use: After page 17 in the text.
Purpose: To develop skill in comprehending phrases which answer questions.

Select the right word from the list below the group of
sentences and put it on the blank lines.

1. Paul _____ his dog many tricks.

2. The dog's _____ was very sore.

3. It was not Tom's _____ that he was late.

4. The baby _____ from room to room.

5. Do you like my new blue _____?

paw   shawl   fault
taught   crawled

Use: After page 17 in the text.
Purpose: To develop and appraise word recognition and word meanings.

25

Read the sentences and draw a line under each true sentence.

1. Some balloons float up and away.

2. Balloons are made like boats.

3. Some balloons get caught in trees.

4. Balloons look like balls.

5. Boys play baseball with balloons.

1. Paula is a girl's name.

2. Paul is a boy's name.

3. Boys are always bigger than girls.

4. Parents are always boys.

5. A daughter is always a girl.

Use: After page 17 in the text.
Purpose: To provide practice in reading critically to determine factual statements.

26

Look at the list of words at the top of the page.
Then write each word under the correct heading below.

kittens	coat	saucer	poodle
glass	suit	skirt	parrot
plate	puppy	pants	bowl

Pets	**Dishes**	**Clothes**

Use: After page 17 in the text.
Purpose: To provide practice in classification of words.

Draw a line around all the words that **may** tell about the picture.

orphan machine child boy	college uncle university school	Phyllis Ralph Philip Dick
ache pain home hurt	dentist doctor spent chemist	Charlotte Jane Dick Phyllis
schooner ball ship boat	pamphlet place booklet book	phone house telephone call
market pharmacy grocery quick	singers chorus soft group	animal elephant nephew large

Use: After page 18 in the text.
Purpose: To develop word meaning using words of recent lessons.

Underline the words where **ph** and **ch** have the same sound as the word at the left.

1. phone	potato	pony	photo	Ralph
2. chorus	chrome	church	chair	school
3. chin	character	charge	chemist	chop
4. chute	machine	Chicago	Charlotte	chest
5. orphan	telephone	telegraph	pills	point
6. elephant	Phyllis	pull	place	Philip
7. schooner	chain	chill	scholar	ache
8. telephone	pamphlet	paper	autograph	page
9. chart	children	chorus	child	character
10. school	chorus	echo	chance	stomach

Use: After page 18 in the text.
Purpose: Auditory and visual discrimination of **ph (f)** words, **ch (k)** words, and **ch (sh)** words.

Put the following words in the right order, using the alphabet to help you.

A B C D E F G H I J K L M N O P Q R S T U V W X Y Z

draw	kept	haul	lawn	uncle
taught	raw	water	even	jumps
some	once	farmer	quickly	blew

_____ _____ _____

_____ _____ _____

_____ _____ _____

_____ _____ _____

_____ _____ _____

_____ _____ _____

_____ _____ _____

_____ _____ _____

_____ _____ _____

_____ _____ _____

Use: After page 18 in the text.
Purpose: To review alphabetizing in conjunction with story words recently studied.

Draw a line under the words which name something you can **see**.

machine	hawk	straw
autograph	squaw	school
call	echo	pause
photograph	saucer	anchor
shawl	elephant	because
ache	awful	scholar

Draw a line under the words which name something you can **hear**.

chorus	saucer	records
quick	call	chestnuts
telephone	noise	singing
orchestra	photograph	straw
gauze	phonograph	crash
echo	squawk	clock

Use: After page 25 in the text.
Purpose: To check the children's understanding of the new words included in this lesson.

Read the sentences. If the sentence is true, put **T** on the line in front of it.
If the sentence is false, put **F** on the line in front of it.

1. _____ My mother is older than I.

2. _____ Seven is a bigger number than nine.

3. _____ We can tell a story.

4. _____ We can look at television.

5. _____ We can listen to the radio.

6. _____ We can dance on the telephone.

7. _____ Teachers go to school.

8. _____ Scholars like to go to school.

Use: After page 25 in the text.
Purpose: To provide an opportunity for the children to respond with understanding to a statement.

Read the two titles and then the words below.   Put the words on the
correct blank lines.   Cross out the words below as you use them.

Animals	Animal Noises
_____	_____
_____	_____
_____	_____
_____	_____
_____	_____
_____	_____
_____	_____
_____	_____

tiger   elephant   barks   moo

mew   baa-baa   fox   howl

                dogs   cows

Use: After page 25 in the text.
Purpose: To promote the ability to make classifications.

Read the sentences silently and select one of the two words below each sentence.   Draw a line around the correct word.

I want to _____
Mother.

telephoned   **telephone**

An _____ can be heard.

endings   **echo**

Scholars like to go
to _____.

cool   **school**

The _____ is a large
animal.

cat   **elephant**

My _____ is a good
boy.

newer   **nephew**

I like the _____ of
Philip.

photograph   **phone**

A _____ is not a real
thing.

person   **phantom**

Did you get his _____?

autographed   **autograph**

Put the _____ on the
boat.

another   **anchor**

The _____ played a
tune.

orchestra   **orders**

Use: After page 25 in the text.
Purpose: To develop visual discrimination of **ph** and **ch** words in a meaningful situation.

34

Read each story and the words under it. Decide which word completes
the story. Write the word on the blank lines.

Paul has something.   Paul has something that is sore.

He can cut with it.   He has a bandage on it.

_____   _____

_____   _____

Paul has a _____.   Paul has a sore _____.

knife   knot   pen   knot   knee   knit

Bob has something.   Phyllis made something.

It is in a cage.   It is for Christmas.

_____   _____

_____   _____

Bob has a _____.   It is a _____.

wren   wrench   wrens   wrong   wreath   wring

Jack made something.   Mother can make something.

He made it with string.   She can make it with yarn.

_____   _____

_____   _____

Jack made a _____.   Mother can _____.

knit   knot   know   knob   knit   knead

Use: After page 26 in the text.
Purpose: To test power of comprehension and promote ability to draw conclusions.

Study the pictures carefully.   Read each sentence.
Decide which word fits the sentence.   Underline the word.
Put the number of the sentence with the correct picture.

1.
Two _____ are in the
 tree.

 wren   **wrens**

2.
The mechanic uses
 a _____.

 wrenches   **wrench**

3.
Hang your _____
 on the hooks.

 wrap   **wraps**

4.
Mother knit a _____.

 shawls   **shawl**

5.
The _____ on the door
 is shiny.

 knobs   **knob**

6.
There are two _____
 in the rope.

 knots   **knot**

Use: After page 26 in the text.
Purpose: To develop the ability to choose either the singular or plural form of the noun.

Read each sentence and draw a line under the word
which completes the sentence.

1. The _____ sells many beautiful jewels.

   grocer   **sailor**   **jeweler**

2. The _____ brings letters to my house.

   pilot   **mail carrier**   **milkman**

3. The _____ makes cakes and rolls.

   barber   **baker**   **banker**

4. The _____ acts in the circus.

   crown   **cowboy**   **clown**

5. The _____ flies the big jet planes.

   pillow   **pilot**   **mail carrier**

6. The _____ works at the TV station.

   mail carrier   **animals**   **announcer**

7. The _____ helps to keep children well.

   daddy   **doctor**   **dentist**

8. The _____ cleans our teeth twice a year.

   writer   **dentist**   **doorman**

Use: After page 26 in the text.
Purpose: To provide practice in reading to make judgments in order to identify missing words in sentences.

Read each sentence and put the correct word on the blank lines.

1. Philip wants to mend broken wrists and knees.   **mechanic**

   _____

   _____

   Philip wants to be a _____.

2. Pam wants to build houses.   **teacher**

   _____

   _____

   Pam wants to be a _____.

3. Ben wants to use screwdrivers and wrenches.   **doctor**

   _____

   _____

   Ben wants to be a _____.

4. Gerald wants to help children.   **carpenter**

   _____

   _____

   Gerald wants to be a _____.

Use: After page 35 in the text.
Purpose: To test powers of comprehension by identifying occupations.

38

What Did They Do? Draw a line under the correct answer in each story.

Phil came home from school. He was tired and hungry. He saw milk and cookies on the table.

Phil ate the snack.

Phil went to bed.

Phil went out to play.

Tom was playing in the yard. It began to rain. Tom crawled under the porch. He had to stay on his knees.

Tom played in the house.

Tom stayed until the rain was over.

Tom stayed in the yard.

Phyllis is too tired to do her school work. She stayed up late the night before. She is unhappy. Phyllis isn't able to do her school work because:

she reads too much.

she stays up too late.

she works too hard.

Use: After page 35 in the text.
Purpose: To provide an opportunity to read for facts and draw conclusions.

Fun on Saturday

The twins, Philip and Phyllis, were going on a picnic. It was a nice sunny day. The lunch was put into a big basket. Mother, Father, and the twins went to a big park.

The basket was full of good things. Philip and Mother set the table. Father and Phyllis took everything out of the car. They ate sandwiches, cake, and fruit. They drank nice cold milk.

The children played games. They waded in the pond, and they had fun with the ducks. They had a wonderful day.

Underline the sentences that are true.

The family went on a hike.

The lunch was in a basket.

They went to a park.

Philip was older than Phyllis.

They played with the ducks.

They had a good time.

Use: After page 35 in the text.
Purpose: To read for details.

40

Read the stories.　　Draw a line around the right word at the end.

Mother and Father Wren made a nest in a tree.　Soon there were three eggs in the nest.　Mother sat on the eggs and kept them warm. One day, three little heads broke out of the eggs.　Mother and Father Wren now had a wren family.

They were

　　　　happy.
　　　　sad.
　　　　cold.

Mother Robin sang from her limb in the apple tree.　Tom Cat crept softly to the tree.　Up and up he climbed. When Mother Robin saw him, she flew away quickly.

She was

　　　　hungry.
　　　　scared.
　　　　tired.

Spring had come and Little Lamb could hear the frogs calling to each other.　He could hear the birds sing. He danced and played in the grass.

Little Lamb was

　　　　cross.
　　　　thirsty.
　　　　merry.

Baby Calf cried for his mother. He had been away from her all day. He had not had his lunch.

He was

　　　　happy.
　　　　hungry.
　　　　chilly.

Use: After page 36 in the text.
Purpose: To provide experience in drawing conclusions concerning emotional reactions.

Draw a line around the correct word.

bomb	thump	climb
come	thumb	click
comb	them	numb
talk	talk	calf
half	walk	call
take	well	calm
hello	last	fireman
half	comb	plumber
calf	lamb	plaything
sidewalk	plum	talk
something	palm	check
streetcar	folk	chalk

Use: After page 47 in the text.
Purpose: To develop meaningful recognition of words having silent **b** and **l**.

Read each story.   Decide which word belongs in the sentence.
Draw a line around the word.

Sam would like something to eat.	Mr. Brown likes to work.
He has a sweet tooth.	He fixes pipes when they leak.
Sam would like	Mr. Brown is a _____.
some _____.	
gum **candles** **candy**	**plumbing** **plumbs** **plumber**
Jack could run very fast.	Tim should like the show.
He has won many races.	It is about airplanes and pilots.
He is a boy who	Tim wants to be
shows _____.	a _____.
speed **speeds** **sheep**	**pillow** **pilot** **pirate**
Mary had a pet.	Children should not walk in the
It was as white as snow.	road.
It was Mary's	It is too dangerous.
little _____.	Children should walk on
	the _____.
limb **lamp** **lamb**	**bedside** **walking** **sidewalk**
I want to write on the blackboard.	Ann likes to climb trees.
I don't want an eraser.	She can climb as fast as a monkey.
I do want some _____.	She is a very good _____.
charts **chalk** **chairs**	**climb** **climbing** **climber**

Use: After page 47 in the text.
Purpose: To promote better comprehension as the children draw conclusions. Also, to provide practice in choice of correct form of words.

Draw a line from a word in the first list to a word in the second list
making a compound word.   Write the new word on the blank lines.
The first one is done for you.

side   where   sidewalk

chalk   board   _____

                            _____

air   walk   _____

                            _____

any   plane   _____

                            _____

care   thing   _____

                            _____

some   other   _____

                            _____

an   less   _____

                            _____

Use: After page 47 in the text.
Purpose: To provide practice with compound words.

Draw a line around the correct number below each word that shows the number of parts (syllables).   The first one is done for you.

granted

1 (2) 3 4

coconuts

1 2 3 4

Florida

1 2 3 4

native

1 2 3 4

anyhow

1 2 3 4

television

1 2 3 4

carrying

1 2 3 4

suddenly

1 2 3 4

climb

1 2 3 4

surprised

1 2 3 4

school

1 2 3 4

plumber

1 2 3 4

walk

1 2 3 4

decided

1 2 3 4

information

1 2 3 4

Use: After page 47 in the text.
Purpose: To provide practice in identifying the number of syllables in a word.

Look at the list of words at the end of each story.
Select the correct words and put them on the blank lines.
Read all the sentences in each box before you put in the words.

Thomas wanted a library card.

_____

_____

He knew he would have to _____ his name
   first. _____

_____

Mother says Thomas _____ his name very well now.
_____

_____

His sister had _____ up for a card last year.

signed   sign   signs

_____

_____

The _____ is getting late.
_____

_____

We must pack _____ bags quickly.
_____

_____

It will take John an _____ to get to the plane.

hour   our   hour

Use: After page 48 in the text.
Purpose: To provide practice in recognition and comprehension of silent, g, and h.

Read the word **bright** and the words in the line below it.
Draw a line under the words that rhyme with **bright**.
Do the same with each group of words.

---

bright

| bring | fight | drink | white | brave | night |

---

gnats

| gnashes | bats | fans | cats | gnaw | gnash |

---

straight

| street | cake | date | struck | late | string |

---

high

| happy | sigh | have | why | cry | hat |

---

taught

| taste | laugh | bake | table | naught | caught |

---

ghost

| game | toast | cost | good | most | post |

---

lighter

| hopes | tighter | biter | look | brighter | lamp |

Use: After page 48 in the text.
Purpose: To give practice in recognition of words with silent letters.

47

Draw a line from each word in the first list to a word in the
second list of nearly opposite meaning.

laugh	low	straight	small
bright	wrong	daughter	truthful
light	dark	foreign	crooked
high	cry	dishonest	son
right	day	large	smooth
night	dull	gnarled	native

Select the correct words and put them on the blank lines.

_____

_____

I do like to _____ letters.

_____   _____

_____   _____

I _____ with my _____ hand.

  right   **write**   **write**   **white**

_____

_____

She is such a cute little _____.

_____

_____

He _____ his dog very fine manners.

        taught   **tot**   **not**

Use: After page 48 in the text.
Purpose: To promote comprehension of antonyms and homonyms and similar sounding words.

Read each sentence.   Draw **one** line under the part that answers the first question.   Draw **two** lines under the part that answers the second question.   The first one is done for you.

Who did something?   What did he or she do?

1. John came home from his vacation.

2. John's sister, Betty, went to a play.

3. Thomas worked in the yard for hours.

4. Father wore a light gray suit to work.

5. Jean told John about her school.

6. Mother called for her daughter and son at school.

7. Uncle Jack hunts and fishes near his home.

8. My daughter taught the little children a song.

Use: After page 49 in the text.
Purpose: To develop an understanding of sentence structure.

Read the verse in each block.   Put the right number on the line
before the day on which you would send that card.

_____ Easter   _____ Mother's Day

_____ Thanksgiving   _____ Hallowe'en

_____ Valentine's Day

1.	2.
Ghosts and witches,	I love you, Mother,
Here and there!	So I want to say
Bats and owls,	How much I love you
Fly everywhere.	On your day.

3.	4.
This is such a happy day,	The Pilgrim fathers
Rabbits and chicks,	Gave us this day.
And bonnets are gay!	To thank our God,
	We all will pray.

5.

Roses are red.

Violets are blue.

I want to say

That I love you.

Use: After page 60 in the text.
Purpose: To develop comprehension of the main idea.

50

Read the story and draw a line under the answer to each question below.

The Thrilling Ride

Bill and Jane were coasting on a hill. Down the hill went the sled. Bill steered. Jane held on tightly. The coasters on the hill watched them. Past trees they whizzed. Jane yelled, "Stop the sled! Stop the sled!" But Bill could not stop it. Suddenly Jane had a feeling that she was a bird in flight. Was she dreaming? She landed in a big pile of snow. Where was Bill? He must have gone all the way down the long slide to the end of the hill. Now, Bill came in sight plodding up the hill. Jane laughed as she called to him. They were so glad to be together. The coasters cheered to see them safe. They went home to tell Mother what a thrilling ride they had had.

1. This story is about

   Dick and Jim   Sally's ride

   Jane's ride   Bill's wagon

2. How did Jane feel as the sled whizzed down the hill?

   cold   scared

   happy   hungry

3. Who sat at the front of the sled?

   Jane   Sally

   Father   Bill

4. How did Jane feel when she saw Bill coming up the hill?

   sad   happy

   tired   cross

Use: After page 60 in the text.
Purpose: To test reading comprehension and vocabulary ability.

Draw a line around all the words in each box that tell about the picture.

light	lad	battle	daughter
night	lamp	fight	girl
day	light	bats	caught

plane	lamb	hour	tame
flight	sheep	out	teacher
plant	lump	minute	taught

Draw a line around the word that has almost the same meaning as the word on the left of each box.

honest	true	fright	scar	gnats	bugs	sign	sight
	time		scare		but		signal
	took		cart		bus		sides

gnaw	nibble	foreign	send	bright	shiny	high	was
	next		see		she		fist
	nest		strange		share		up

laugh	giggle	slight	little	sight	yard	straight	even
	give		left		yes		end
	guess		fell		eyes		all

Use: After page 60 in the text.
Purpose: To increase the meaningful vocabulary.

Add a word that has a similar meaning to each row of words.
Choose a word from the list.   Cross out the word as you use it.

_____

1. Christmas   Thanksgiving   Easter   _____

2. chews   gnaws   nibbles   _____

3. pulling   dragging   carrying   _____

4. yellow   green   purple   _____

5. squash   cabbage   carrot   _____

tugging   **bites**   **pumpkin**   **Hallowe'en**   **orange**

Use: After page 60 in the text.
Purpose: To promote the ability to classify, using the new words of recent lessons.

53

Read the rhymes and put the number of the rhyme
with the matching picture.

1. Over in a valley lived a
      boy named John.
   In his new red wagon,
      he rode on and on.

2. We chose a pumpkin
      round and yellow,
   And now we have this
      smiling fellow.

3. Little Bunny Rabbit liked
      his carrots raw,
   Went to the farmer's garden
      to gnaw and gnaw and gnaw.

4. Polly dressed up
      like a ghost,
   And put her pumpkin
      on the post.

Put the rhyming words on these lines:

_____   _____   _____   _____

_____   _____   _____   _____

_____   _____   _____   _____

_____   _____   _____   _____

Use: After page 61 in the text.
Purpose: To facilitate fluency and comprehension through rhymes.

Read the riddles and write the answers on the blank lines.
The answer must rhyme with the word in the box.

Mary wears me on
   her head.
She does not put me
   on in bed.

_____

_____

I am a _____.

| that |

I am an animal,
Big and brown.

_____

_____

I am a _____.

| wear |

I am good fruit.
I am juicy and sweet.

_____

_____

I am a _____.

| bear |

Mother mends with me.
I am not a needle.

_____

_____

I am _____.

| head |

I am light and fluffy,
But a warm coat for
   the birds.

_____

_____

I am a _____.

| weather |

Today is fair,
No clouds, no rain.

_____

_____

Today is _____.

| pheasant |

I am used to make shoes
And belts and coats.

_____

_____

I am _____.

| weather |

Use: After page 62 in the text.
Purpose: To use the new words in context meaningfully in a rhyming situation.

55

Vocabulary Test

1. head	2. thread	3. dear	4. read	5. really
heads	three	deed	raid	ready
hear	there	dead	real	reads

6. beast	7. dears	8. spread	9. breeze	10. lead
best	deaf	spells	bread	learn
breast	drag	spoils	breath	leaps

11. held	12. dreadful	13. wheel	14. mean	15. feather
help	helps	weeks	meant	father
health	dread	wealthy	means	follow

16. please	17. mellow	18. break	19. heart	20. heavy
pleasant	mean	breath	heard	heads
plans	meadow	breaks	hearth	heading

21. leaks	22. seeds	23. early	24. heard	25. break
learn	such	earth	hear	beak
leaps	search	earns	hears	dream

Use: After page 62 in the text.
Purpose: To test recognition of **ea** words. (Words to be dictated are on the back cover of the Teacher's Edition.)

Put the correct words on the lines.

_____

_____

_____

After the storm, the trees were _____.

_____

_____

The boy ran, and the _____ chased him.

bear   **bare**

_____

_____

_____

I want a new _____ of shoes.

_____

_____

This _____ tastes very good.

pair   **pear**

_____

_____

_____

Please _____ the paper neatly.

_____

_____

Do you use your _____ hand?

write   **right**

Use: After page 62 in the text.
Purpose: To give practice in the ability to choose the correct homonyms.

**If ea spells the short sound of e in the underlined word, put S in the box.
Put L in the box if the underlined word has an ea that spells long e.**

1. Today I will <u>read</u> this book. ☐

2. I <u>read</u> a poem to the class last week. ☐

3. I hope we have fair <u>weather</u>. ☐

4. Mother made three loaves of <u>bread</u>. ☐

5. My <u>head</u> is aching from the noise. ☐

---

1. The bed was made of <u>feathers</u>. ☐

2. She <u>meant</u> to go home last week. ☐

3. The <u>teacher</u> is absent today. ☐

4. Your <u>health</u> is very important. ☐

5. Do you think the leg will <u>heal</u> soon? ☐

Use: After page 63 in the text.
Purpose: To give practice in differentiating between the long and short e spelled ea.

58

Draw a line from a word in the first list to a word in the
second list to make a compound word.

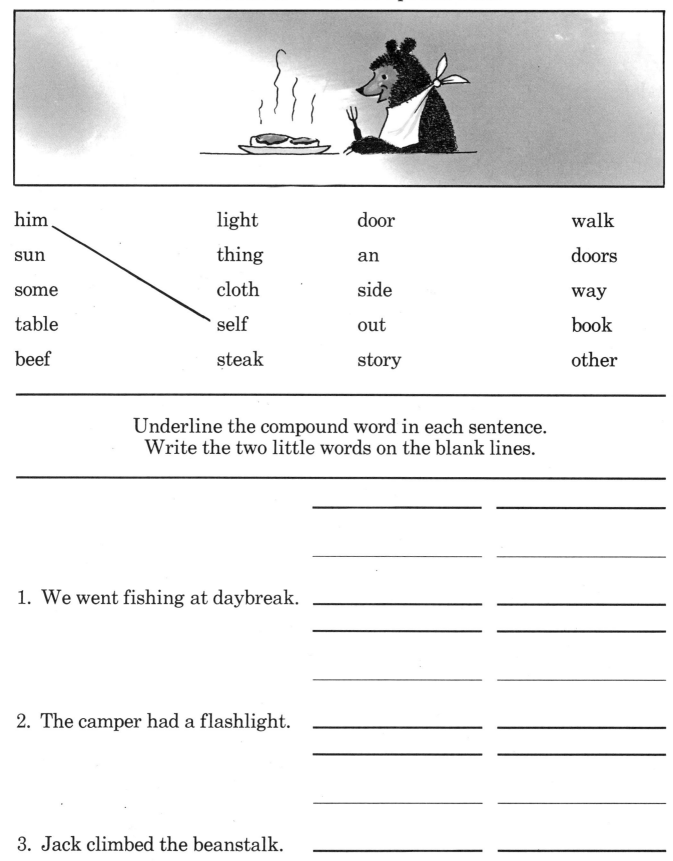

him	light	door	walk
sun	thing	an	doors
some	cloth	side	way
table	self	out	book
beef	steak	story	other

Underline the compound word in each sentence.
Write the two little words on the blank lines.

_____ _____

_____ _____

1. We went fishing at daybreak. _____ _____

_____ _____

2. The camper had a flashlight. _____ _____

_____ _____

3. Jack climbed the beanstalk. _____ _____

Use: After page 71 in the text.
Purpose: To promote the ability to recognize parts of compound words.

Say the name of each picture. If you hear one syllable (part), write **1** in the box. If you hear two syllables (parts), write **2** in the box.

Use: After page 71 in the text.
Purpose: To check the children's auditory recognition of syllables. Identify the pictures before having the children work.

60

Read the groups of sentences below.   Number the blocks at the right
so that the events are in the right order.

He lost the steak in the water. ☐

He went to look for food. ☐

Once there was a big bear. ☐

He found some nice juicy steak. ☐

Now she is lonely and sad. ☐

There once was a naughty little girl. ☐

She screamed at the other children. ☐

So they would not play with her. ☐

Polly looked everywhere for her. ☐

Polly had a pretty little kitten. ☐

When she found her, Polly scolded her and took her home. ☐

The kitten ran away one day. ☐

John opened all his packages. ☐

Then John was a very happy boy. ☐

Mother bought him five toys for his birthday. ☐

John did not have many toys. ☐

Use: After page 71 in the text.
Purpose: To give an opportunity for the children to arrange stories by proper sequence.

Vocabulary Test
Read the words in each box.   Draw a line under the rhyming words.

fierce piece pierce	chief niece thief	wreath grief brief
leak shell speak	either never neither	thunder bundle blunder
bunnies berries cherries	stores stories shores	shrieks shakes speaks
candles candies handles	kitties cities kittens	field fierce shield
niece priest piece	crumb lamb thumb	selling telling ceiling
heart part heard	could cold would	take talk chalk

Use: After page 72 in the text.
Purpose: To test the ability to identify rhyming words; also visual and auditory mastery of words presented.

Read the story. Circle all the possible answers.

Bonnie went for a	lilies	daisies	violets
walk in the woods.	stories	bunnies	cookies
It was spring.	cities	beach	berries
She saw _____.	trees	candies	birds

Mother went to get dinner.	berries	people	lilies
She put things on the table.	cake	meadow	bread
She had _____.	school	carrots	pears
	pie	celery	mice

Susie went to the	daisies	library	kitties
farm. She ran to	clover	cake	calves
the meadow.	steak	lambs	neighbors
She saw _____.	cities	puppies	ponies

Use: After page 72 in the text.
Purpose: To give practice in classifying and drawing conclusions.

Read each group of words and the phrases under it. Underline the correct phrase to finish each sentence.

Phyllis wore a wreath	Tom put the puppy's food
on her shoe.	in a book.
on her head.	in a bowl.
on her table.	in a hat.
Ned placed the cake	Mother put the steak
on the roof.	on the grass.
on the floor.	on the plate.
on the table.	on the chair.
Penny put the ponies	The flowers grew
in the house.	in the yard.
in the barn.	on the floor.
in the tub.	in the chair.
The pears grew	The autograph was signed
on the hat.	by an animal.
on the tree.	by an actor.
on the ground.	by a rabbit.

Use: After page 72 in the text.
Purpose: To draw conclusions to complete sentences. To comprehend content.

Read the phrases listed below. Put the phrases that tell what you **see** under the "Using My Eyes" column, and the phrases that tell what you **hear** under the "Using My Ears" column.

1. wreaths of flowers

2. a pretty fawn

3. a rooster crowing

4. beds of pansies

5. a clock ticking

Using My Eyes

Using My Ears

Use: After page 72 in the text.
Purpose: To improve phrasing and to comprehend context. It is also a review of vocabulary.

65

Read the story and draw a line under the phrase or word
which answers the question.

Blue Flower

Sky Chief was a brave Indian chief. All his people loved him. He had a little niece, Blue Flower. She looked just like her name. Her eyes were as blue as the sky. ·Her hair was black and shiny, and it waved in the wind like the tall prairie grass. She could run like a deer, and she loved all the animals of the forest.

Blue Flower had a pet fawn. They played in the fields in the warm summer. She made wreaths of daisies for her pet. They had fun in the snow in the cold winter.

Sky Chief admired his little niece very much. On cold winter evenings, he told her stories about the stars and how they got in the sky. He told her of the Sun God and the Rain God, too.

Little Blue Flower was a very happy girl and she made all the others around her happy as well.

Where did Blue Flower play?
    in the trees
    in the fields
    in the mountains

What animals did she love?
    none
    one
    all

What did she make for her pet?
    clover wreath
    daisy wreath
    lily wreath

What happened on cold winter nights?
    Sky Chief went hunting.
    Sky Chief told stories.
    Blue Flower played games.

What did she learn about?
    the Sun God and the Rain God
    the hunting trips
    the pet fawn

Was her life happy?
    no
    yes
    sometimes

Use: After page 77 in the text.
Purpose: To provide practice in reading for information, using material from the new lesson.

Read the question. Look at each picture. Underline the phrase or word that you think answers the question.

Where?

at the circus

at the library

in the forest

in Chicago

in a box

in the lake

in the forest

in the library

at the store

at the airport

at the mountains

at the train

in the cage

in the street

in the trees

on the train

on the peanut

on the prairie

Who?

noisy children

children in school

checker players

airplane

airplane pilot

airport

Indians

into

Irene

machine

mechanic

macaroni

grass

plumber

grocer

doctor

doll

door

Use: After page 77 in the text.
Purpose: To test understanding of the new vocabulary.

Read the sentences and choose the correct word from those listed below the sentences. Underline the word.

The _____ makes the noise.

   thunder   **lightning**

We like to _____ brief stories.

   read   **reading**

Phyllis _____ pansies, daisies, and lilies.

   gathers   **gathering**

The chief did not look _____.

   pierce   **fierce**

Blue Flower gathered water _____.

   lilies   **limbs**

Mother _____ a telephone call.

   received   **receiving**

Do you _____ in ghosts?

   believes   **believe**

She made _____ of daisies.

   briefs   **wreaths**

Sky Chief told _____ about forest animals.

   stores   **stories**

Father _____ the ceiling blue.

   painting   **painted**

Did you _____ a fierce scream?

   hears   **hear**

Blue Flower _____ there was a thunderbird.

   behaved   **believed**

Use: After page 77 in the text.
Purpose: To provide practice in choosing correct words to complete sentences.

Read each sentence and draw a line around the right word.
Write the word on the lines.

The puppy belongs to them.   theirs

_____

_____

He is _____ .   they

Santa's big animals pull the sleigh.   reindeer

_____

_____

They are his eight _____ .   rainbow

Mother has a pretty net on her hat.   veil

_____

_____

She calls it a _____ .   vein

My horse, Danny, makes a loud noise   neighbor

_____

_____

when he sees me. He _____ .   neighs

In winter, Danny gives me rides   sleigh

_____

_____

in a big red _____ .   slide

Use: After page 78 in the text.
Purpose: To use context clues in discrimination of words having **ei**.

Write the correct words on the lines as you select them
from the group of words below.

I _____ my dinner before going out.

There were _____ children at the party.

eight   **ate**

Put the rubbers over _____.

I want to dry _____ clothes.

their   **there**

It _____ nearly every day lately.

The rider held the horse's _____.

rains   **reins**

Use: After page 78 in the text.
Purpose: To provide practice with homonyms, using words having the new phonetic elements, **ei** and **eigh** as long **a**.

Copy these words in alphabetical order in the spaces below. The first one is done for you.

celery	sleigh	uncle	freight	six	piece
awful	zebra	eighty	image	quiet	hawk

1. awful

2. _____

3. _____

4. _____

5. _____

6. _____

7. _____

8. _____

9. _____

10. _____

11. _____

12. _____

Use: After page 78 in the text.
Purpose: To give practice in arranging words in alphabetical order.

Read each sentence and draw a line around the correct word to complete the sentence.

We laugh at the

day
clown
loud
drown

Many people live in the

barn
store
city
door

The top of the room is the

certain
celery
sand
ceiling

Mice are small

aunts
animals
people
boys

There is money in the

bank
bread
ball
band

The boy's name is

Grace
Good
Game
Gerald

We like to look at

spill
television
trips
stops

The train was at the

cars
trains
station
state

The turtle moves

loudly
slowly
fast
fair

The bear can

grows
glove
good
growl

Use: After page 86 in the text.
Purpose: Reading Test 1—Sentence and word meaning.

Read each sentence and draw a line around the correct word to complete the sentence.

There are seven days in a

year
day
week
weed

In winter we see

blow
snow
grow
slow

I want to join the

club
climb
trap
drop

Blue is a pretty

cold
cost
color
caller

The dew is on the

glass
grab
grass
glad

A pew is a seat in a

church
chin
chop
chair

Father will drive the new

tractor
antlers
answers
mechanic

John is busy in

school
soon
spoon
score

Play the record on the

phonograph
phone
photograph
telegraph

I want to sing in the

cross
chorus
shore
care

Use: After page 86 in the text.
Purpose: Reading Test—Sentence and word meaning.

Underline the correct word or words to complete each sentence.

John has a pair of white rabbits. He feeds them every day.

1. John has two _____.

   cats   rats   mice   rabbits

2. The rabbits are _____.

   white   while   wide   wild

John has a sister, Sally. Sally is five years old. John is two years older.

3. Sally is John's _____.

   brother   twin   uncle   sister

4. John is Sally's

   older _____.

   sister   brother   friend   cousin

Both John and Sally went to school. Sally was in kindergarten. John was in the second grade. His teacher's name was Miss Smith. Sally's teacher was Mrs. Jones.

5. Sally went to _____.

   town   kindergarten

   first grade   visit

6. John was in the _____.

   second grade   first grade

   third grade   show

7. John's teacher

   was _____.

   Miss Smith   Mrs. Smith

   Mrs. Jones   Miss Jones

One day John and Sally went to the circus. They saw elephants and trained horses. They laughed at the clowns and fed the monkeys.

8. The children fed

   the _____.

   horses   lions   money   monkeys

9. The clowns made

   them _____.

   laugh laughed train laughing

10. The horses at the circus

   were _____.

   fine   trained   tall   trains

Use: After page 86 in the text.
Purpose: Reading Test 2—Paragraph meaning.

Vocabulary Test

1. rein reins reining	**2.** rumble reindeer rascal	**3.** vain veil vase	**4.** vein veins very	**5.** reigns rings reign
6. were we're weigh	**7.** neigh neighbor neighs	**8.** weight weighs weights	**9.** eight eighty eighteen	**10.** eating eighty eighteen
11. nice nets neigh	**12.** fries freight flies	**13.** sleigh sleds ships	**14.** there they them	**15.** grey grind grease
16. price prey play	**17.** chief cheese choose	**18.** times thief tease	**19.** thieves thief these	**20.** bleed bread brief
21. shield shed shine	**22.** grind grief glee	**23.** grieve grave give	**24.** cries cities city	**25.** kitties kites kitten

Use: After page 87 in the text. (See inside back cover of the Teacher's Edition for words to dictate.)
Purpose: Vocabulary Test.

Underline all the words having a **short** vowel.

master	make	chest
here	twin	guns
fire	from	pure
pond	grand	hope
must	save	swim

Underline all the words having a **long** vowel.

came	fans	take
tree	cold	butter
spend	time	fence
she	chop	wise
fuse	music	camp

Underline all the words having the **ie** that spells **long e.**

chief	field	thief
pie	thieves	cries
pieces	tries	fierce
niece	fiercely	shriek
fries	fields	their

Underline all the words having the **ei** and **ey** that spell **long a.**

eight	they	ceiling
either	reins	veil
neither	their	sleigh
reindeer	receive	eighty
weigh	weather	eighteen

Use: After page 87 in the text.
Purpose: Review of long and short vowels and discrimination of vowel sounds in **ie, ei,** and **ey** words.

Read each sentence and draw a line around
the correct word to complete the sentence.

To mind means to

| over |
| obey |
| other |
| owned |

A warm month is

| February |
| December |
| January |
| June |

We go to school on

| Saturday |
| March |
| Monday |
| Sunday |

Every house has a

| robin |
| roof |
| road |
| rode |

We look through a

| wind |
| window |
| walk |
| wins |

We don't like
stormy

| wishes |
| wells |
| west |
| weather |

It takes twelve
things to make a

| dozen |
| dose |
| does |
| dress |

People grow things
in a

| game |
| garden |
| house |
| cabin |

Farmers live in the

| city |
| country |
| store |
| circus |

You use a pen to

| wrote |
| right |
| write |
| ride |

Use: After page 95 in the text.
Purpose: Reading Test 3—Sentence and word meaning.

77

Read each sentence and draw a line around
the correct word to complete the sentence.

The little boy fell
and hurt his

elf
cellar
elbow
elephant

I have candy, but I
want ice cream

to
toot
too
two

The funny picture
made everyone

cry
laugh
last
laughs

The lion was not
hungry after he
had

eating
eat
eaten
drinks

There are sixty
minutes in an

home
house
hour
second

To look for something
means to

see
search
send
serve

The lion liked to
eat raw

meet
meal
meat
melt

She told all the
stories she

new
knew
mew
know

We eat breakfast
in the

bathroom
kitchen
bedroom
hall

The opposite of
huge is

big
tall
fat
tiny

Use: After page 95 in the text.
Purpose: Reading Test—Sentence and word meaning.

78

Read the story silently.   Then read the sentences under the story.
Draw a line around **Yes** or **No** after each sentence.

Many years ago, when Grandfather was a boy, the children walked a long way to school. They rode in a sleigh in the winter. Big Black, the work horse, pulled the sleigh over the squeaking snow. The bells on his harness jingled merrily and the children, wrapped in warm scarves and caps and mittens, reached the school with rosy cheeks and smiling faces.

Grandfather was once a little boy.   Yes   No

He lived next to the school.   Yes   No

The children rode on a scooter to school.   Yes   No

The horse had sleigh bells on his harness.   Yes   No

The children had a happy time riding to school.   Yes   No

Use: After page 102 in the text.
Purpose: To provide practice in gaining understanding from silent reading.

Find the compound words.   Draw a line to separate the two words.
Put each word on the blank lines.

Example: Sally has a
play|house.

play   house

1. Spot has a new
   doghouse.

2. Dan must dust the
   schoolroom.

3. I wanted to read this
   afternoon.

4. I can't find my book
   anywhere.

Draw a line from the word on the left to one on the right
which will make a compound word.

any	bow
rain	yard
school	noon
after	way

Use: After page 102 in the text.
Purpose: To provide further practice in recognition of compound words.

Read each phrase and underline those which tell something about the words that are at the top of each group.

The Three Bears	Goldilocks	In the Bears' House
three brown bears	a little girl	a pretty house
a little bee	pretty flowers	three chairs
Baby Bear	yellow hair	Goldilocks slept
She made a pot of porridge	a tiny house	a big hard bed
went for a walk	she went in	a tiny soft bed
an angry voice	ate all of it	down the road
on the roof	fell fast asleep	over the moon
They looked in the bedroom	ran home	in their bedroom

Use: After page 113 in the text.
Purpose: To give practice in phrasing and classification.

Read the phrase on the left and find one on the right that will make
a whole sentence.   Draw a line from one phrase to the other.

THE THREE BEARS

Once upon a time	in the forest.
They lived	golden yellow hair.
Mother Bear	so she went in.
Goldilocks had pretty	she got home.
The door was not locked	fell fast asleep.
Goldilocks lay down and	made a pot of porridge.
She ran until	there were three bears.

Write the correct word in each sentence.   Read all the sentences
before you put in the words.

_____

_____

1. Once upon a time there was a fuzzy little _____.

_____

_____

2. His favorite fruit was a big juicy _____.

_____

3. Sometimes he ate too many, I _____.

fear   bear   pear

Use: After page 113 in the text.
Purpose: To give experience in phrasing and sentence structure; also to review in context words which are similar in appearance.

Once there were three bears who lived together in a little house in the forest. The biggest bear, named Tubby, worked hard all day finding berries and good things to eat for himself and his friends. The middle-sized bear, called Fuzzy, worked hard too, getting the honey from the bee-trees. The third bear, who was called Cuffy, just rolled and played in the sun all day.

One day, Tubby and Fuzzy went deep into the forest to find food. They said, "Please come with us, Cuffy, we will be gone for a long time." But Cuffy said, "No, thank you. If I go with you, I will have to work hard. I will stay here and play until you get back."

So off went the two bears, and Cuffy played with the rabbits and the chipmunks. But soon he began to get hungry, and asked the rabbits and the chipmunks if he could have lunch with them. But the rabbit said he had to go to Farmer Brown's garden for carrots. Cuffy knew he could not do that. Little chipmunk was going to run down into his storeroom in the ground, and Cuffy knew he could not go there. Poor Cuffy! How hungry he was for some nice sweet berries. "Next time," he said, "Just wait until next time! I will be glad to go and find food with Fuzzy and Tubby."

Put a number in each box to show in what order these things happened.

☐ Cuffy asked the rabbit and the chipmunk for some lunch.

☐ Cuffy decided that he would be glad to go with the bears the next time.

☐ Tubby and Fuzzy went deep into the forest to find food.

☐ Once there were three bears who lived together.

Use: After page 113 in the text.
Purpose: To read a new story with understanding and to arrange ideas in sequence.

Draw a line around the correct word.

travel
trim
velvet

vegetables
violet
vinegar

bunch
build
bridge

straw
string
raw

turnips
turn
ribbon

branch
bucket
bundle

weather
window
meadow

wolf
were
work

burning
churning
build

children
chimney
chicken

Use: After page 125 in the text.
Purpose: To provide an opportunity for word recognition using picture clues.

Read the sentences and put an X in the box after the ones that are correct.

The three little pigs went out into the world. □

The three little pigs went out for a swim. □

The first little pig ran to his brother's home. □

The first little pig was eaten by a wolf. □

The second little pig built himself a pretty home. □

The second little pig built himself a funny store. □

The third little pig built a strong house of bricks. □

The third little pig built a huge house of stone. □

The wolf invited the little pig to go to the turnip field. □

The wolf invited the little pig to go to the cabbage patch. □

The pig was up in a plane when the wolf got there. □

The pig was up in the apple tree when the wolf got there. □

The wolf started to climb down the chimney. □

The wolf started to climb down the blackboard. □

Little Pig put a pot of hot water in the apple tree. □

Little Pig put a pot of hot water under the chimney. □

Use: After page 125 in the text.
Purpose: To provide practice in reading for fine detail.

Underline the correct word or words and complete the sentences.

John knew how to read. He was in the second grade. He read stories to Sally. Sally liked the stories. She liked the story of <u>Robbie Rabbit</u> best. Then she liked to hear about The Three Bears. Sally knew some nursery rhymes. She knew <u>Baa, Baa, Black Sheep</u> and <u>Mary Had A Little Lamb</u>.

_____

_____

1. Sally knew many _____.

numbers   names   problems   nursery rhymes

_____

_____

2. Best of all, Sally liked the story of _____.

toy dogs   The Three Bears   Robbie Rabbit   The Three Pigs

_____

_____

3. John could read but Sally _____.

went home   sang songs   sang   could not

_____

_____

4. <u>Robbie Rabbit</u> and <u>The Three Bears</u> are _____.

stories   stores   rhymes   shops

Use: After page 138 in the text.
Purpose: Reading Test 4—Paragraph meaning.

Match the words by putting the number on the line.
The first one is done for you.

travel	**3**	1. lived	carry	___	1. building
huff	___	2. walked	walk	___	2. carrying
blaze	___	3. traveled	build	___	3. looking
boil	___	4. blazed	look	___	4. walking
live	___	5. boiled	come	___	5. blowing
walk	___	6. huffed	blow	___	6. coming

Put a number in each box to show in what order each thing happened.

Use: After page 138 in the text.
Purpose: To provide practice in working with base words and their endings.

Underline the correct word or words and complete the sentences.

John had a friend whose name was Fred. He lived next door. Sally had a friend who lived in the house next to Fred's. Her name was Pauline. Pauline had a kitten. His name was Tommy. He was black and white. Fred had a yellow dog named Randolph. Randolph and Tommy fought as cats and dogs usually do. Tommy could always climb a tree when he had had enough.

_____

_____

1. The name of Sally's friend was _____.

    Randolph   **Paul**   **Pauline**   **Tommy**

_____

_____

2. Randolph was a yellow _____.

    friend   **boy**   **kitten**   **dog**

_____

_____

3. Tommy was a little _____.

    kitten   **color**   **children**   **colder**

_____

_____

4. Pauline lived in the house next to _____.

    Fred   **Pauline**   **Sally**   **John**

Use: After page 138 in the text.
Purpose: Reading Test 4—Paragraph meaning.

Read each story and draw a line under one of the three phrases
which completes the story.

Three little pigs played in the
sun. They rolled and rolled until
they were tired.
Then they

1. slept in the warm sun.

2. ate a big dinner.

3. went to the store.

Three little monkeys played leap
frog. They jumped over each other
and swung from tree to tree.
They liked these games because
it was fun to

1. eat a banana.

2. swing by their tails.

3. make a nest.

Three little rabbits hopped into
Mr. Brown's garden. They wanted
to find something good to eat. They
soon found what they wanted.
They found

1. a tree to swing on.

2. a fine bed of lettuce.

3. a hole in a tree.

Three little puppies sat on a mat
outside the door. They wanted to
go in. They barked quiet little
barks, then they barked bigger
barks.
Then

1. they ran away.

2. the door opened for them.

3. they drank some water.

Use: After page 138 in the text.
Purpose: To give an opportunity for the children to read and draw conclusions.

Draw a line from each sentence to the matching picture.   Put a number in the box in front of each sentence to show when these things happened.

☐ Robbie falls on top of all the tomatoes.

☐ Robbie Rabbit has to take a bath.

☐ Four little rabbits live with their mother in a house near a big forest.

☐ Robbie Rabbit is looking at the blueberry pie.

☐ Mrs. Bird comes to visit.

☐ Robbie is sweeping the floor.

Use: After page 138 in the text.
Purpose: To review the story just read and give practice in sequential arrangement.

Vocabulary Test

1. cheat chief cheek	2. thieves thief these	3. fierce field fields	4. yield years year	5. sheet sheep shield
6. city cities cries	7. eight eighteen eighty	8. freight freeze fences	9. neighbors neighbor neighborly	10. weighs weight weigh
11. berry berries bending	12. carried carry carries	13. panther pansies pansy	14. believed believes belief	15. travel travels traveled
16. reason reasons seasons	17. sounding sound sounds	18. different differently direction	19. twins twelve twenty	20. written writing writes
21. break breaks breaking	22. heavier heaven heavy	23. teaching teacher teach	24. signs signed sign	25. bright night right

Use: After page 138 in the text. (See inside back cover of the Teacher's Edition for words to dictate.)
Purpose: Vocabulary Test.

Look at each picture.   Put in the missing letters to complete each word.

_____ ore

_____ ess

_____ urch

_____ ow

_____ ack

_____ ock

_____ ant

_____ eel

la _____

ra _____

wa _____

sa _____

Use: After page 138 in the text.
Purpose: To review initial and final blends.

92

Read each question and find the book in which you could find the answer. Write the number of the book on the space after the question. Find the stories in the Table of Contents in your book and put the page number under each book.

1.

2.

3.

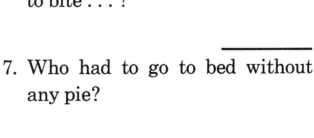

4.

1. Who broke a chair and fell asleep in a strange bed?
_____

2. Who listened to stories of the stars in the sky?
_____

3. Who lost his beefsteak when he tried to grasp his reflection?
_____

4. Who had a stomach ache from eating too much?
_____

5. Who caught his beautiful antlers in a tree branch?
_____

6. Who wanted to make something with "Big eyes to see and teeth to bite . . . ?"
_____

7. Who had to go to bed without any pie?
_____

8. Who built his house of bricks?
_____

5.

6.

7.

8.

Use: After page 138 in the text.
Purpose: To review the stories in the book just completed, and to review the use of the Table of Contents.

WHY ARE THESE PICTURES FUNNY?
Draw a line under the best answer.

1. The farmer has no hat.

2. The farmer is milking a horse.

3. The farmer is milking a cow.

1. The children are wearing bathing suits in the snow.

2. The children are playing in the snow.

3. The bathing suits are not in the water.

1. A rabbit is digging a hole.

2. A squirrel is climbing a tree.

3. A rabbit is climbing a tree.

1. Jack is giving his sister a ride.

2. Jack's wagon is upside down.

3. Jack's wagon cannot go fast.

1. Ned and Tom forgot their fish poles.

2. Ned and Tom are fishing in a boat.

3. Ned and Tom are playing tennis.

Use: After page 138 in the text.
Purpose: To give opportunities for sentence comprehension, and to see absurdities in picture interpretation.